Volume One.

Virginia State Garrison Regiment
of Williamsburg

MUSICK OF THE FIFES & DRUMS

Compiled and Arranged by John C. Moon, Musickmaster
with the assistance of
Herbert E. Watson and William E. White

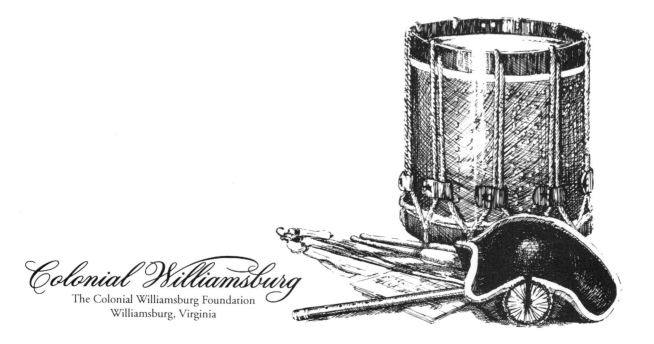

Colonial Williamsburg
The Colonial Williamsburg Foundation
Williamsburg, Virginia

© 1976 by The Colonial Williamsburg Foundation
All rights reserved. Published 1976

18 17 16 15 14 13 12   13 14 15 16

Printed in the United States of America

Library of Congress Cataloging in Publication Data
Main entry under title:
Musick of the fifes and drums.
    At head of title: Virginia State Garrison Regiment.
    CONTENTS: v. 1. Quick marches.
    1. Fife and drum music. I. Moon, John C.
II. Watson, Herbert, 1941–   III. White, William E.
M1270.M94   788'.51'5   75-19259
ISBN-13: 978-0-87935-031-4
ISBN-10: 0-87935-031-8

*Colonial Williamsburg is a registered trade name of
The Colonial Williamsburg Foundation, a not-for-profit
educational institution.*

The Colonial Williamsburg Foundation
PO Box 1776
Williamsburg, VA 23187-1776
www.history.org

TABLE OF CONTENTS

PREFACE

A fifer and a drummer were officially—and necessarily—attached to each company of men in both European and American military forces in the colonial era. In camp they sounded all the various duty calls, mostly routine but occasionally emergency calls. In the field, whether on maneuvers or in battle, they signaled the movements and actions ordered by their officers.

The earliest reference so far found in American sources to ceremonial massing of fifers and drummers under the leadership of a fife major or drum major occurs, appropriately, in Washington's general orders for August 23, 1777. Preparing to move southward to meet the British forces then disembarking at the head of Chesapeake Bay, the American commander in chief felt strongly that his army should march through the center of Philadelphia. He hoped that a brave show would put heart in the patriots there, give pause to the Tories, and persuade the uncommitted. Accordingly, he not only set forth the order of march and the route, but also specified in great detail the desired appearance and comportment of the men. Near the close of his long order came a paragraph decreeing that:

> The drums and fifes of each brigade are to be collected in the center of it; and a tune for the quick step played, but with such moderation, that the men may step to it with ease; and without *dancing* along, or totally disregarding the music, as too often has been the case.

The final phrase indicates that there had been more than one previous instance of massed parade music, though no record of any seems to have survived. The custom was widespread and of long standing in European armies, however, having been launched by the Swiss in the early sixteenth century. In the British army by 1786, according to *Grose's Military Antiques*, "Beside a Drum Major to each Regiment, there is now, and has been for some time, a Drum Major General to the Army,..." appointed to supervise the individual players and the corps en masse.

Manuals for the fife first appeared in America in the late eighteenth and early nineteenth centuries. These collections contained hundreds of popular airs, many of them used for military purposes. The tunes were often of folk origin, Irish and Scottish melodies being especially prominent.

Only in 1812 did drumming books and manuals appear, coincidentally, in both England and America: in London *The Art of Beating the Drum* by Samuel Potter, drum major of the Coldstream Guards, and in Washington *A New, Useful and Complete System of Drum-Beating* by Charles Stewart Ashworth. These books employed a musical tablature or shorthand needing interpretation. Other manuals, such as David Hazeltine's *Instructor in Martial Music* of about 1820, used plain English to explain the drum beatings to accompany scored fife parts. That was the way von Steuben's drill regulations had done it; for example, "First Serjeant's Call—one roll and three flams." Often the modern director must use his own good sense of eighteenth-century style to achieve an acceptable rendition.

During most of the Revolution, Virginia was not an active theater of war. Therefore Continental troops were stationed in Williamsburg only for a short time—just before the siege of Yorktown. State units, however, were raised for local protection, and the Virginia State Garrison Regiment was such a unit, active from 1778 to 1781. Its headquarters were in Williamsburg through most of the period, and its area of responsibility was the eastern portion of the state. By adopting the role of the re-created musical element of that regiment, the Colonial Williamsburg Fifes and Drums can rightly represent much of the Revolutionary period.

Many gaps remain in the history of fifing and drumming in America. We cannot aver that every note we play in Colonial Williamsburg is authentic, though that is our aim. We hope that the music herein will be regarded as an historically valid interpretation as well as one that excites its hearers even today.

SOURCES OF THE MUSIC

Beck Manuscript   Tunes 2, 4, 10, 11

A bound manuscript volume in the Music Division of the
Library of Congress (photostat in the Colonial Williamsburg
Fifes and Drums library). The flyleaf proclaims it to have been
"Mary Mathers Book. 1810," while an interior page bears the
inscription, "Copied by Henry Beck in the Year 1786."
Nothing is known of Henry Beck's identity, and it would
appear doubtful (if the inscription is in his hand) that he
copied anything more than the index.

Playel's Rondo   Tune 12

Playel's rondo is from *Entire New and Compleat Instructions for the
Fife, Containing the Best and Easiest Directions to Learn That
Instrument with a Collection of the Most Celebrated Marches Airs
&c.* London: Printed for John Preston [ca. 1778 – 1787].

Cushing   Tunes 1, 5, 7, 10

*The Fifer's Companion. No. 1 Containing Instructions for Playing
the Fife, and a Collection of Music, Consisting of Marches, Airs, &c.
With their seconds added.* Salem (Mass.): Printed by Joshua
Cushing [1804?].

Deisenroth   Tune 9

A collection of military music from 1685 to 1823 arranged by
Friedrich Deisenroth. A reprint of volumes 2 and 3 (and per-
haps others) was issued in 1961 by Rud. Erdmann, Bonn. The
Colonial Williamsburg Fifes and Drums library has photoprints
of some of the selections, but little information about the
original publication from which the copies were made.

Greenwood Manuscript   Tune 3

A manuscript volume (photostat in the Colonial Williamsburg
Fifes and Drums library), identified on the title page as that of
John Greenwood, fife major at the age of fifteen in the 15th
Massachusetts regiment, 1775 and 1776. A later entry by John
Greenwood's son Isaac asserts that it was given to the elder
Greenwood by a British fife major. John Greenwood (1760–
1843) later became a dentist, having George Washington as
one of his patients. Selections used with permission of the
New-York Historical Society, which has the original.

Handel's *Warlike Music*   Tune 8

[George Frederick Handel] *Warlike Music. Book I: Being a Choice
Collection of Marches & Trumpet Tunes for a German Flute, Violin,
or Harpsichord. By Mr. Handel and St. Martini and the most
eminent masters.* London: Printed by I. Walsh [1760?].

Fifes

1. BOSTON MARCH

A typical example of simple four-measure divisions that are easy to memorize. The tune is taken from *The Fifer's Companion*, issued by Joshua Cushing in or about 1804. (Both fife and drum arrangements have been made by J.C.M., the drum part taken from eighteenth-century open beatings.)

1

1. BOSTON MARCH

Fifes

2. BRITISH GRENADIERS

A popular song and march from the late seventeenth century. Of unknown origin, it bears a strong resemblance to the Dutch tune "William of Nassau" (1581). (The fife part was arranged by W.E.W. from the Beck Manuscript, part 1, of about 1784; the drum part was written by George Carroll and arranged by J.C.M.)

2. BRITISH GRENADIERS

Drums

3. CHAIN COTILLION

*C ♮ in original manuscript

A dance, as its name indicates, which translates well into march tempo. It is taken from the Greenwood Manuscript of about 1776. (The fife part was transposed by J.C.M.; the drum part was arranged by George Carroll.)

3. CHAIN COTILLION

Drums

4. CUCKOO'S NEST

The arrangement for fifes, an excellent fingering exercise, comes from the prodigious Beck Manuscript, part 1. (The fife arrangement was made by W.E.W.; that for the drums by J.C.M.)

4. CUCKOO'S NEST

Drums

8

Fifes

5. FIRST OF SEPTEMBER

* G in original

Obviously written as a march, the fife music comes from Cushing's *Fifer's Companion* (1804). The significance of the title date seems to have been lost. (J.C.M. arranged the drum part to fit the original fife music.)

5. FIRST OF SEPTEMBER

Drums

6. HEY! JOHNNIE COPE
ARE YE WAUKEN YET?

A Scottish marching tune written to satirize the English general caught unprepared at daybreak during the 1745 Jacobite uprisings. Many Scottish regiments today use the tune as their duty call for reveille. (Both parts were arranged by J.C.M., who learned the tune during his service in the British army; no formal source is known.)

6. HEY! JOHNNIE COPE
ARE YE WAUKEN YET?

7. LA PROMENADE

1st fife

2nd fife

An interesting French dance in 6/8 time and in five separate sections, written this way, no doubt, to fit the dance steps. The fife part comes from Cushing's *Fifer's Companion* (1804). (Drum part arranged by J.C.M. to fit the fife music.)

7. LA PROMENADE

Fifes

8. LUXEMBURGHS MARCH

One of many marches written by George Frederick Handel in recognition of various dignitaries and performed often at Vauxhall Gardens in London. This arrangement is a transposition from a military band score found in Handel's *Warlike Music, Book I,* published presumably in 1760. (Both parts arranged by J.C.M.)

8. LUXEMBURGHS MARCH

Drums

9. MARSCH DER PAPPENHEIMER REITER

A fine example of a Prussian regimental march—in this
case of the Pappenheimer cavalry—requiring staccato
tonguing to produce the best results. It is taken from
Deisenroth. (The fife part was arranged and transcribed
by J.C.M.; the drum arrangement is by R. Edmonson and
J. Barbour, snare and bass drum section leaders.)

9. MARSCH DER PAPPENHEIMER REITER

Drums

10. NEW GERMAN SPA

This is another example of how well a folk tune adapted for dancing can be re-adapted for marching purposes. The fife part comes from Cushing's 1804 *Fifer's Companion;* the drum part from the Beck Manuscript. (Both parts arranged by J.C.M.)

10. NEW GERMAN SPA

Drums

11. OVER THE WATER TO CHARLEY

This is another Scottish traditional song dating from the Young Pretender's rebellion against the English crown. It comes from the Beck Manuscript, part 1. (Drum part arranged by J.C.M. to fit the original fife music.)

11. OVER THE WATER TO CHARLEY

Fifes

12. PLAYEL'S RONDO

Playel (or Pleyel) was a prolific composer who produced many tuneful movements. This rondo is included in *Entire New and Compleat Instructions for the Fife, Containing the Best and Easiest Directions to Learn That Instrument with a Collection of the Most Celebrated Marches Airs &c.*

12. PLAYEL'S RONDO

Drums

D.C. al .$.